Daily Humor in Russian Life
Ежедневный Юмор в Русской Жизни

Russian caricatures with English translations
Русские карикатуры с английским переводом

Volume 7 - Watch Out Children
Том 7 - Осторожно Дети

Author: Foxy Dime
Автор: Фокси Дайм

Volume 7 - Watch Out Children
Том 7 - Осторожно Дети

Author: Foxy Dime
Автор: Фокси Дайм

This book is dedicated to the bright memory of my father, who inspired me to reach higher and never stop learning.

Эта книга посвящена светлой памяти моего отца, который вдохновлял меня достигать большего в жизни и никогда не прекращать учиться.

INTRODUCTION

The illustrations in this book were created by my father, who passed away in 2016. I decided to publish this series anonymously, since everything shared in this book, I hold very dear to my heart.

In reality my papa loved children. I remember when we were little, every weekend we would start with same sentence, "Take us to an interesting place". My papa patiently started listing places: the park, to the fountains, and so on. I still remember all the time my papa spent helping me create a miniature copy of the church for my class project. The miniature copy came out very beautiful and the teacher put it on a display behind a glass showcase. Just as years later I would help my daughter with her many school projects…

There are a few caricatures in the book referring to the Soviet Union era. All school kids age 9 to 15 were expected to join the Pioneers. There were no exceptions. The Pioneer attire included a red tie scarf and pin badge. Pioneers were taught to prioritize Communism above all and had motto всегда готов! (vsegda gotov! "Always Ready!"). There are a few caricatures related to the pioneers. These caricatures would never be allowed to be published in the Soviet Union. But here we are years later and we can freely smile at these caricatures.

There are many caricatures in this book referring to Pinocchio. The Russian version of Pinocchio is different. There is a wonderful old Soviet Movie "Pinocchio" (Buratino). In this movie Pinocchio has friends, Malvina and poodle Arlekino, as well enemies, fox Alisa and cat Basilio.

Of course, every reader of this book probably experienced a child saying something mean and embarrassing. But because they are children, we scold them and laugh. All these wonderful drawings as always reflect kind humor expressed through my father's art.

ВСТУПЛЕНИЕ

Иллюстрации в этой книге нарисованы моим отцом, который скончался в 2016 году. Я решила опубликовать эту книгу анонимно, так как содержимое этой книги очень близко и дорого моему сердцу.

Мой отец очень любил детей. Я помню, когда мы были маленькими, каждую субботу мы начинали с предложения: - «Давай пойдём в интересное место». Мой папа терпеливо перечислял разные места: парк, фонтаны и так далее. Я помню, как мой папа потратил кучу времени, помогая мне с конструкцией миниатюрной копии церкви для проекта в школе. Миниатюрная копия вышла очень красивой, и учительница выставила её на дисплей, за стеклянной витриной. Вот и я, годы спустя, также помогала моей дочке с её школьным проектом.

В этой книге включены несколько карикатур советских времен. Все дети от девяти до пятнадцати лет должны были стать пионерами. Все без исключения. В наряд пионера объязательно входил красный галстук и значок. Пионеров учили ставить коммунизм в первую очередь, и у них был девиз «Будь готов! Всегда готов!». Эта серия также включает в себя карикатуры пионеров. В советское время эти карикатуры никогда бы не разрешили опубликовать. Но времена изменились и мы свободно можем рассматривать эти карикатуры.

В советские времена был заснят замечательный фильм «Буратино». В этом фильме у Буратино есть друзья Мальвина и пудель Артемон, а также так же враги лиса Алиса и кот Базилио. Русская сказка о Буратино отличается от других версий. Эта книга включает в себя несколько карикатур с Буратино.

И конечно же кто не испытывал неловкое состояние от смущающей фразы, сказанной ребенком. И именно потому, что это дети, мы их поправляем и за одно смеёмся. Все эти картинки отражают добрый юмор моего отца.

CARICATURES

КАРИКАТУРЫ

-On this image the crocodile laid her eggs. Who can tell me why?
-He is old; they don't need them any more… (Play on the words, in the Russian language produce eggs have the same name as male testicles)

-Which one is yours?
-What's the difference, tomorrow I have to bring him back.

-Why is father destroying books?
-He isn't destroying them; he is creating new ones!

-This's hard work unlike surfing the internet...!?

-O wow, my mama will be so surprised; she has been telling you something on the phone for the last hour…

-Grandpa, how many times is five times twenty?
-Are we buying or selling?

-My baby, take the paperclip from the door lock, - you're going to poke our curious neighbor's eye out...

-Puppy pooped in the corner again....
-Where else is puppy to poop? In the cabinet drawer? I poop there...
(In the reference to the famous Russian cartoon "The little boy and Carlson")

-O my God, he tears up the first draft of my first novel…
-Did you teach him how to read?

-I will tell your papa…
-Papa! Uncle Petya wants to talk to you…

-Vova, give us example of when a solid form of substance turns into gas form without going through its liquid forms.
-Beans!

-Mam, kids at school teasing me, telling me that my mouth is too big…
-Don't cry my son, get the ladle and let's go eat borscht!

-Children are life's flowers! I gathered the bouquet and gave them to grandma.

-Papa, please fix the drums...
-I don't know "dum-dum" in drums...

-You promised us a reward for the missing dog... Pay me advance and I will start looking for her...

-Did you hear last night that the baby was snoring really loud? -Don't worry they're "breathable" diapers.

-How did
your violin
break?
-I was
learning
composition
and
suddenly it
fell out the
window…

-Mam,
prepare your
second
breast for
the evening,
I will have
company…!

-Vovochka, quit spinning!
-Marivanna, if you want to live, be able to spin!

The notebook, that boy holding in his hand called «дневник» (dnevnik). In this notebook teaches mark grades.
-The main thing that we're healthy, there is peace, love in the family, isn't that true papa?)

-In his intellectual development Pinocchio is an oak…!
-That's not true he made from pine…

-I don't understand, did I have a son or did I plant the tree?
(In reference to a Muslim saying that a man needs to have a son, build a house and plant a tree)

-In our times music had more melody…
-Grandma, that is the mixer…!

-Mam, why did the stork bring my little sister, and I was found in the cabbage patch?
-The stork couldn't bring you all the way into the house…

-We need to call the piano tuner, "sol" isn't playing…
-How many times do I have to tell you; don't turn the piano into dinner table…
(Play on the word sol, which also means salt)

-If you love me, then marry that guy!

-In our house my papa decided everything, and my mama decided who will be our papa!

-Did your papa miss me while I wasn't home?
-Not at the beginning, but closer to your arrival – very…!

-Son, why do you have an "F" grade for all subjects other than geography?
-There was no homework yet for geography…

Writing on the board: "Learning is light and ignorance is darkness!"
-If learning is light, then a teacher is a lantern.

-It's not good behavior to look into keyhole!
-And is it good behavior to show nasty things in a keyhole?

-Son, who told you that you're a schizophrenic?
-Flies!

-Tanya, join us to build a sand castle! I would gladly join you, but my education doesn't allow me!

-Mama asked me to tell you that my papa went fishing and I'm going to play in the yard...

-Grandpa started acting like a child and my papa got him a doll…

-Papa, mama is telling us that she needs the chair…

-Whose statue should I place on piano – Beethoven or Bach…?
-Place the Beethoven, he's deaf…

-There you go grandma, we crossed the road with you, now you can keep going by yourself?

-Hello… Do you need papa? Who's asking? His boss? Which boss are you? The old goat or the smelly goat?

-Stop picking your nose, you might scratch your brains and you will forget all of us!
-I'm picking my nose not too deep…

-Happiness is when kids aren't hungry, have cloths to wear, and they aren't home…!

-Olechka don't squash ants, they have little kids too; they're waiting for mama…
-And mama won't come… And papa won't come…

-Go ahead, show papa where you buried papa's keys?

-What did you do with papa's wallet?

-We get our parents at such an age; it's impossible for them to stop bad habits!

-Papa! I was born in winter… Storks are not flying, cabbage isn't growing… Where did I come from?
-We downloaded you from internet…!

-Grandson, do you know which mushrooms are good and edible and which are poisonous?
-Yes, these are edible, and these are for the farmer's market...

-My baby, go to the kitchen and check on what Vashya is doing, then tell him immediately to stop...

-That's my brother…
-And that's my grandmother…

-Are you sure that they told you to get two kilos of candy and 100g of carrots?

-Papa, give me money to go to the zoo and look at the pythons…
-Take a magnifying glass and go to the garden and look at the worms.

-На…! I bet you like to poop…!?

Sign on the
machine:
"ATM"
-Is papa
sitting
there?

-My
daughter,
please bring
a few plates
and rolling
pin. We need
to explain
something
to your papa
in a cultured
manner…!!

-Can you please give me the bread rolls with puppy seeds?
-Maybe I should give you loaf with hash? (Sarcastically)

-Vovochka, how do you know that papa got his paycheck today?
-He took pickled cucumbers…

-Papa, after pea soup can we play "Guess the melody?"

-Interesting, how do you know all these nasty things you exhibit to our daughter…?!

-Papa Geppetto, hurry and nail down the little tube; I have to pee...!!

- Papa Geppetto, please cut out a girl for me... Malvina ran away with Arlekino...!! (In the Russian version of "Pinnochio" Mal'vina and Arlekino are supporting characters).

-Do you want to become a paratrooper?

-Vasya, where is the door? How is the bird supposed to get to her nest?
-She is already there...!!

-Mam, can fire run around?
-No, that's the car owner burning…

-My vision is negative five…
-Are your eyes cold?

Буратино не ходи в школу, тебе еще нет семи. Сейчас мы тебе точно скажем, сколько тебе...!

-Pinocchio, you don't need to go to school; you're not seven yet. Now we will tell you exactly how old are you...!

Вовочка, а как ты стал генералом, если в школе ни хрена не знал?

А я и сейчас ни хрена не знаю... Но, к утру чтоб все было сделано...!

-Vovochka, how did you become a general, if you didn't know anything in school?
-I don't know anything now either..., but everything needs to be done by morning...!

-P'ero, are you sure Pinocchio and Beaver can become best friends…

-Oh, Pinocchio, even now he continues to give us warmth… (In Russian version of "Pinnochio" Malvina and Arlekino are supporting characters).

-Mam, are we going to salt the borsch?

-I'm coming, as soon as "dnevnick" (notebook with teacher's greats) finish burning I will be there…

-Grandma, why do you have such bad teeth? -Tooth decay!

-Your papa mixed everything up. He has horns and not wings…!

Writing on the building: "Wine and vodka factory" -Can we stop there…

-Three percent return guaranteed …!!

-You can buy organic milk only here!

-You told me a fortune that I will have three kids and a husband…
-I got three kids and when will I get a husband?

-Can you tell the engine driver to slow train down? My Vasya can't keep up with counting the telephone poles.

-Your papa looks as beautiful as part of a toilet interior…

-How come the teakettle can whistle and I can't?

-Don't make a mess, respect someone else's labor!
-My mama isn't someone else!

-Careful, I bite!

-Don't let cat out of the refrigerator; he is being punished…!

-This's Big Ben…
-It looks like Big Ben is a clock…!

-Help me climb out. I'm in the swamp because of you. Once I climb out, I will marry you…!
-Sign and I will help you!

-Even bells need a good hung clapper…!

-Papa, why is the violin without strings? -Not everything at once, when you learn how to play, then we will get you the strings…

-Papa Geppetto, I have constipation.
-Quickly, get a chisel!

-How many times did I tell you, don't play with matches...?!
-I'm not playing: I'm lighting my cigarette.

-Since you broke the window, we will have to use your butt to seal it…
-Mam, will you replace me at dinner time?

-Yes, this's my son. Can you bring him an hour later? We're having a party…

-Grandpa, why can't children watch this film?
-Sit down, you will see why…

-Vovochka, who won the Crimean war? The Russians or Turkey?
-Ukrainians, who have Crimea now that's who the winner is.

-It looks like they added veneer and polished the image.

-Pinocchio, knowledge is light!

-Papa, is off-road zone intended to be drive free and cars have to drive on the sidewalks and lawn…?

-Papa, I don't know what I want, but I want two of everything…!

-Take me to be a Pioneer, I'm made from redwood.

-Children, start multiplying, I need wood for winter…

CONCLUSION

Our passion is to spread the knowledge of the mysterious Russian language. We created educational and entertaining materials for learning Russian. You can find our educational materials in both printed and digital format on our website, on Amazon, Amazon Kindle, Apple Books, Barnes and Nobles, and Google play books. Be sure to visit our website for more information!

Our Website	https://foxitdimensions.com/
FoxIT Russian Alphabet Cards	https://foxitdimensions.com/russian-alphabet-cards.html
FoxIT Russian Alphabet Poster	https://foxitdimensions.com/russian-alphabet-poster.html
FoxIT Russian Alphabet Book	https://foxitdimensions.com/russian-alphabet-book.html

Daily Humor in Russian Life Series	https://foxitdimensions.com/russian-humor-books.html
Volume 1 - Mix	https://foxitdimensions.com/daily-humor-in-russian-life-volume-1.html
Volume 2 - Mix	https://foxitdimensions.com/daily-humor-in-russian-life-volume-2.html
Volume 3 - Alcohol Edition	https://foxitdimensions.com/daily-humor-in-russian-life-volume-3.html
Volume 4 - Rated "R" edition	https://foxitdimensions.com/daily-humor-in-russian-life-volume-4.html
Volume 5 - Beware of doctors	https://foxitdimensions.com/daily-humor-in-russian-life-volume-5.html
Volume 6 - Our Smaller Brothers	https://foxitdimensions.com/daily-humor-in-russian-life-volume-6.html
Volume 7 - Watch Out Children	https://foxitdimensions.com/daily-humor-in-russian-life-volume-7.html
Volume 8 - Love and Marriage	https://foxitdimensions.com/daily-humor-in-russian-life-volume-8.html
Volume 9 - Woman's Touch	https://foxitdimensions.com/daily-humor-in-russian-life-volume-9.html
Volume 10 - Man's Power	https://foxitdimensions.com/daily-humor-in-russian-life-volume-10.html
Volume 11 - Eat and Drink	https://foxitdimensions.com/daily-humor-in-russian-life-volume-11.html
Volume 12 - Man vs Woman	https://foxitdimensions.com/daily-humor-in-russian-life-volume-12.html
Volume 13 - Mix	https://foxitdimensions.com/daily-humor-in-russian-life-volume-13.html
Volume 14 - Mix	https://foxitdimensions.com/daily-humor-in-russian-life-volume-14.html

ЗАКЛЮЧЕНИЕ

Наша миссия - это распространять знание таинственного русского языка. Мы создали учебные и занимательные материалы для изучения русского языка. Вы можете приобрести их в книжном или электронном формате на нашем сайте, на Амазоне, на сайте книжного магазина Barnes and Noble, в книжных магазинах Google (EBooks) и Apple (IBooks). Читайте подробности на нашем сайте.

Наш сайт	https://foxitdimensions.com/
Русские Алфавитные Карточки	https://foxitdimensions.com/russian-alphabet-cards.html
Постер с Русским Алфавитом	https://foxitdimensions.com/russian-alphabet-poster.html
Книга Русский Алфавит	https://foxitdimensions.com/russian-alphabet-book.html

Ежедневный Юмор в Русской Жизни	https://foxitdimensions.com/russian-humor-books.html
Том 1 - Ассорти	https://foxitdimensions.com/daily-humor-in-russian-life-volume-1.html
Том 2 - Ассорти	https://foxitdimensions.com/daily-humor-in-russian-life-volume-2.html
Том 3 - Алкогольное Издание	https://foxitdimensions.com/daily-humor-in-russian-life-volume-3.html
Том 4 - Издание с рейтингом «16+»	https://foxitdimensions.com/daily-humor-in-russian-life-volume-4.html
Том 5 - Берегитесь врачей	https://foxitdimensions.com/daily-humor-in-russian-life-volume-5.html
Том 6 - Братья Наши Меньшие	https://foxitdimensions.com/daily-humor-in-russian-life-volume-6.html
Том 7 - Осторожно Дети	https://foxitdimensions.com/daily-humor-in-russian-life-volume-7.html
Том 8 - Любовь и Женитьба	https://foxitdimensions.com/daily-humor-in-russian-life-volume-8.html
Том 9 - Прикосновение Женщины	https://foxitdimensions.com/daily-humor-in-russian-life-volume-9.html
Том 10 - Мужская Сила	https://foxitdimensions.com/daily-humor-in-russian-life-volume-10.html
Том 11 - Ешь и Закусывай	https://foxitdimensions.com/daily-humor-in-russian-life-volume-11.html
Том 12 - Мужчина против женщины	https://foxitdimensions.com/daily-humor-in-russian-life-volume-12.html
Том 13 - Ассорти	https://foxitdimensions.com/daily-humor-in-russian-life-volume-13.html
Том 14 - Ассорти	https://foxitdimensions.com/daily-humor-in-russian-life-volume-14.html

Printed in Great Britain
by Amazon

39216614R00034